Solo and Duet Books

For the Piano

Collected and Harmonized,
Edited and Fingered
by ANGELA DILLER
and ELIZABETH QUAILE

FIRST SOLO BOOK
New Edition

SECOND SOLO BOOK
New Edition

THIRD SOLO BOOK

FOURTH SOLO BOOK

FIRST DUET BOOK

→ SECOND DUET BOOK
New Edition

THIRD DUET BOOK

G. SCHIRMER, Inc.

DISTRIBUTED BY

7777 W. BLUEMOUND RD. P.O. BOX 13819 MILWAUKEE, WI 53213

ED. 3024

PREFACE

The Second Solo Book and Second Duet Book have two objects:

(1) To provide, from the beginning of the child's piano study, material of permanent *musical value* which shall serve as a basis for the development of his taste.

With the exception of a few preliminary exercises, all the pieces in these Books are either folk-tunes that have been sung by generations of children, or classics that should be part of every child's musical experience.

We believe that the child can be interested very early in his musical career in different styles of composition so we have used folk-tunes of many nations, modal tunes, chorales, etc., including, from the beginning, pieces of irregular metrical structure, i.e., not confined to the usual two- and four-measure phrase-lengths.

Music of this character cannot be heard too often, and we feel sure that the teacher as well as the pupil will appreciate the absence of original "teaching pieces."

(2) To provide a plentiful selection of pieces of real musical interest so carefully graded, both musically and technically, that the child is stimulated but not overtaxed.

The necessary foundation for the artistic playing of any instrument is a musical ear. Pianoforte-playing in itself cannot, by any means, be relied upon to furnish this, as the attention of the child is necessarily focused upon the overcoming of technical difficulties. Therefore, it is recommended that the child be given a large experience of music before he begins the study of an instrument. Just as language is learned first by hearing and then by speaking and reading, so music should be learned by experiencing it before learning to read or to perform on an instrument. Singing is the natural mode of musical expression and learning to sing a large number of good songs "by ear" will greatly broaden the child's musical horizon. When he thus has had actual experience of music, he will be more interested in learning to read and to play.

ANGELA DILLER

ELIZABETH QUAILE

FOREWORD TO THE 1976 REVISED EDITION

In preparing the new edition of the Second Duet Book we have tried to maintain in every way the musical character and high standards of the work as Miss Diller and Miss Quaile envisaged it.

The changes have been very few, the most important one being the substitution of conventional slurs for the square brackets in duets with melodies of a predominantly legato and flowing character.

We hope this edition will continue to bring pleasure to new generations of piano students and will help to stimulate an interest in the world's great piano literature.

Dorothy Weed
Teacher at the Diller-Quaile School of Music
1922 to the present
Music Director 1955-1972

Robert Fraley
Teacher at the Diller-Quaile School of Music
1961 to the present
Director since 1972

TABLE OF CONTENTS

Second Duet Book

SECONDO

The Poppies

Waltz

Franz Schubert

attacca

Second Duet Book

PRIMO

The Poppies

Allegretto

(Pupil)

1

The pop-pies in my gar-den grow And they will make a love-ly show;

I've picked a mil-lion of them here, And send them all to you, my dear.

Waltz

Franz Schubert

Moderato

2

attacca

4

Polly Oliver

Andante con moto

English Folk-Tune

3

PRIMO

Polly Oliver

Andante con moto

English Folk-Tune

(Pupil)

3

Polish Song

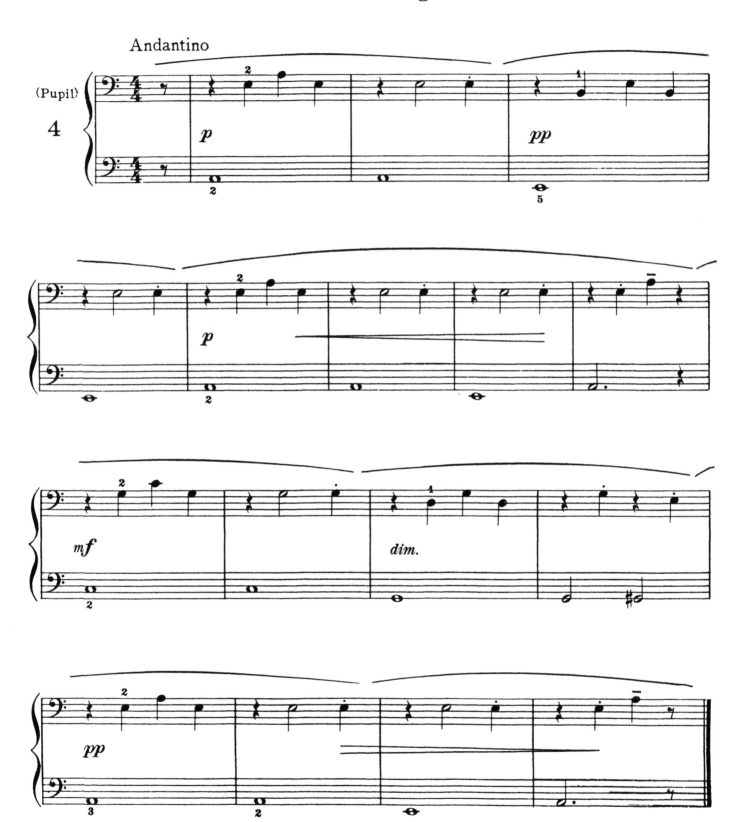

PRIMO

Polish Song

Chorale: Liebster Jesu

Johann Rudolf Ahle
Harmonized by J.S.Bach

PRIMO

Chorale: Liebster Jesu

Johann Rudolf Ahle
Harmonized by J. S. Bach

The Foggy Dew

Irish Tune

PRIMO

The Foggy Dew

Irish Tune

Rowing in the Boat

English Folk-Tune
(Adapted)

Rowing in the Boat

English Folk-Tune
(Adapted)

SECONDO

Newcastle

Allegretto

English Country-Dance

(Pupil)

8

Newcastle

Allegretto

English Country-Dance

SECONDO

Lota is Dead

Allegro

Swedish Folk-Dance

PRIMO

Lota is Dead

Swedish Folk-Dance

SECONDO

Here We're Skipping up the Scale

Here We're Skipping up the Scale

Chorale: Lobt Gott, ihr Christen

Nicolaus Herman
Harmonized by J. S. Bach

Row Well, Ye Mariners

English Country-Dance

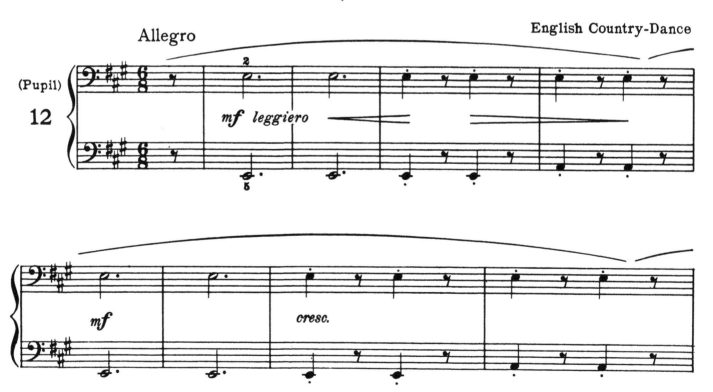

Chorale: Lobt Gott, ihr Christen

Nicolaus Herman
Harmonized by J. S. Bach

Row Well, Ye Mariners

English Country-Dance

The Chimes of Dunkirk

Moderato

English Folk-Tune

13

PRIMO

The Chimes of Dunkirk

English Folk-Tune

Moderato

(Pupil)

13

Singing Game

English Folk-Tune

Allegro

The Oak and the Ash

Moderato sostenuto

Old English Song

(Pupil)

Singing Game

English Folk-Tune

The Oak and the Ash

Old English Song

Boatman's Song of the Volga

Russian Folk-Tune

PRIMO

Boatman's Song of the Volga

Andante con moto

Russian Folk-Tune

SECONDO

The Meeting of the Waters

Andante con moto

Irish Tune

Haste Thee, Nymph

Allegro

After Dr. Arnold

The Meeting of the Waters

Irish Tune

Haste Thee, Nymph

After Dr. Arnold

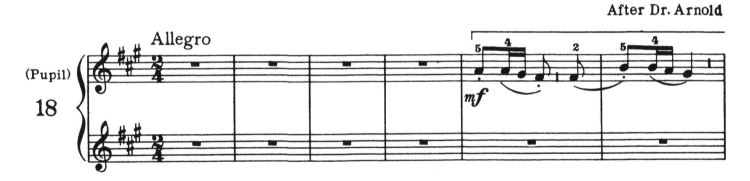

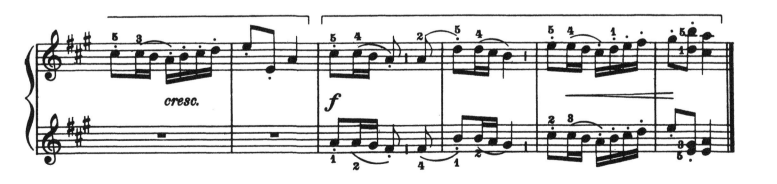

SECONDO

Van Diemen's Land

Allegro con brio

Old English Ballad

(Pupil)

19

PRIMO

Van Diemen's Land

Old English Ballad

Hark, the Tiny Cowslip Bell

English Folk-Tune

Allegretto

20

PRIMO

Hark, the Tiny Cowslip Bell

English Folk-Tune

Amaryllis

Old French Melody

Andantino

21

Pastorale

Old French Melody

Allegretto con grazia

22

PRIMO

Amaryllis

Andantino

Old French Melody

Pastorale

Allegretto con grazia

Old French Melody

SECONDO

SECONDO

Hark! the Summons

Allegro marcato

Welsh Folk-Tune

23

PRIMO

Hark! the Summons

Welsh Folk-Tune

Greensleeves

Old English Tune

Greensleeves

Old English Tune

The Fiddler

German Melody

The Fiddler

German Melody

Flora's Song

French Melody

Allegretto con grazia

Flora's Song

Allegretto con grazia

French Melody

Loch Lomond

Scotch Air

PRIMO

Loch Lomond

Scotch Air

Tambourin

Old French Tune

28

Tambourin

Old French Tune

The Hawk Swoops on High

Highland Tune

The Hawk Swoops on High

Con spirito

Highland Tune

(Pupil)

29

Chorale: Nun ruhen alle Wälder

Heinrich Isaac
Harmonized by J. S. Bach

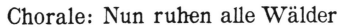

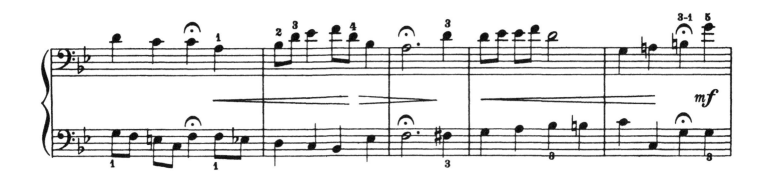

Charlie is my Darlin'

Scotch Folk-Tune

Chorale: Nun ruhen alle Wälder

Heinrich Isaac
Harmonized by J. S. Bach

Charlie is my Darlin'

Scotch Folk-Tune

SECONDO

Aria from "The Magic Flute"

W.A. Mozart

PRIMO

Aria from "The Magic Flute"

W.A.Mozart

Andantino

(Pupil)

32

SECONDO

Valses nobles

I

Franz Schubert

Allegro con spirito

Valses nobles

I

Allegro con spirito

Franz Schubert

(Pupil)

33

SECONDO

II

PRIMO

II

SECONDO

III

Allegro

PRIMO

III

SECONDO

IV

Andantino

SECONDO

V

Allegro con brio

PRIMO

V

Allegro con brio